The Painted Clown

KATY WELLS

ISBN: 9798735079958

ABOUT THE AUTHOR

Having studied a degree in English Literature and Early Childhood studies- specialising in early years education and SEN, Katy began a teaching career in 2000. Upon completion of her KS2/3 PGCE (ages 7 years to 14 years) she has been an educator working within mainstream settings, where the levels of special educational need and vulnerable children have been well above the national average. This memoir style novella is based upon observations of her own daughter, who is on the Autistic spectrum, although undiagnosed. In addition, Katy has used her experience and knowledge spanning two decades of working with young people with Autism- within mainstream educational settings.

CONTENTS

The Painted Clown.

Chpt 1: Who am I?

I had been the geek, the book lover, the dancer, the academic, the sports fanatic, the food guru, the makeup expert. I had been whoever I had needed to be. Whichever role I had played, had depended on who I had been with. My personas changed so readily. My survival had depended on my ability to adapt, to perform…..to mask.

What I am though, is more complicated. On the surface, I allow you to see a typical teenage girl but don't be fooled by my smiles- for underneath, I have many, many layers. What I am is possibly undefined, possibly overlooked: a victim of a doctor's research years ago which focused mainly on boys. Has society improved any further since then? Does it choose to challenge the stereotypical and gender biased views which exist regarding Autism? My experience tells me not. Often, I have wondered if having a formal diagnosis of Autism would have made my life more bearable. People tend to know what to do with a label- read the instructions and act accordingly. But what did people do with me? There was no reference to what temperature I could be washed at or whether I could be ironed or not. Did I need dry cleaning? Or was I to be put on a quick wash and hope for the best- that I wouldn't be harmed and damaged in some way; I wouldn't become misshapen and an ugly reminder of what I might have been with better care?

I had little choice but to carry on as best as I could, forging a route through the confusion and fear. I had become the chameleon. Happily, I had blended into the forefront or background. I had feigned indignation at what I hadn't understood; laughed at what I had loathed and smiled to mask my fears. My body might have blazed red or green, or even yellow if this had been preferred- I had always aimed to please. It frustrated me that society hadn't recognised what was in front of their very eyes; perhaps my disguises had been just too effective- after all, I have had years to perfect my deceit. If only I had been looked at more closely, people may have seen through my façade. If they had, they would have seen me. The real me. My exterior front would have been broken and I would have been exposed as the girl struggling with undiagnosed ASD. A fraud maybe, a cheat possibly, a liar…but still a girl crying out to be recognised and understood for the quirks I had and the struggles I strove to overcome.

Chpt 2: The role of 'The Dancer'

I am not going to lie because it is not something I have ever had the ability to do easily. When I claim to be a pretty damn good dancer it is because I am. That bit of me is real- I had never faked that. That part of me is genuine. Authentic. There's a pattern to dancing- a sequence: 5,6,7,8 and I'm off. Surreptitiously, I had watched the other girls and copied of course- I had been a shape shifter who became the same as those around me. Or better even. The lines of the bodies in the mirror assisted... I had observed without being noticed. Reflections after reflections had bounced across the glass and I took note. It was the small things I had noticed- the extra extension in the arm to add grace and a touch of finesse, the slight tilt of the head. Grand battement. Pas de chat. Pirouette. I had watched it all. The beat of the music ran through my veins and I felt the melody pulsating alongside my own heartbeat- it had guided me too and of course, I followed. If only my early teenage life had been as constant as dancing- where every bend, stretch and leap had a clear name, action and beat. A routine. Order. Structure.

I had become so good in this role that acquaintances could be excused for misunderstanding me. How could I be anywhere on the spectrum when I had performed as well as I had? I should have been more modest I guess- but I hadn't been. I had never done modesty very well, but I had learnt how to pretend to be modest. Nobody likes a vain bitch, do they- or so I have learned? I was a good dancer- fact- and my exam results had been a testament to that.

"Look how confident she is!"

"She's such a performer!"

It had all been totally ironic of course, as people had been totally unaware of my inner turmoil every time I stepped foot on stage or walked into the exam studio. Anxiety had built up like an almighty crescendo inside of me- easily surpassing the pianist on stage left. I had often imagined a whole range of scenarios happening: all of them had ended in disaster- my costume unpinning and exposing my prepubescent breasts, my hair piece falling out, forgetting my steps, slipping or tripping……. I had waited in the darkness of the curtained wing, wishing the folds of heavy material would wrap me safely inside like a chrysalis. But it was right to call me a performer- for I had emerged like a beautiful butterfly; I fluttered across the stage despite wanting to hide in the warmth of enveloping darkness. I was a dancer though, and that is what dancers did- they performed. They learned, they practised, they got it right.

I had been performing at life for many years. It was just that people chose to ignore the level and depth of my performances. They had gone further than the application of red lipstick, ghastly blue eyeshadow and the fake smile. In dancing, I had been told what to do- explicit steps and moves. My dance teacher, a classic example from a bygone age, had been just perfect for my needs. Just the right combination of love and strictness had worked for me. More red lipstick. Left leg higher. Extend that arm. 'Show face'. Add more bronzer. 5,6,7,8. She said it and I had done it- it must be known that

I have never been a rule breaker. Even now-I do as I am told. Always. I had become so good at putting on a show that performing to a real audience was second nature. I had blended into the chorus line. We had all looked the same and we all did the same- there was no margin for error or breaking rank. I had practised so hard to be perfect that I made few. Tits and teeth- I had it sorted.

Of course, there had been other areas of dance that had caused me much anxiety. The dressing room situation at a dance performance had always been an incessant struggle. Imagine a small room full of ten to twelve excited yet nervous teenagers. Boxes upon boxes of costumes and accessories claimed the most space. Helpful chaperones had done their best to organise everyone, but it could only be described as a form of organised chaos. Sequined bows had been counted and recounted; white satin gloves had been paired and sorted in size order. Two hours later, there had been a mad panic as it was discovered that there had been something missing- and we were due on stage at any moment.

"I thought you counted them?" one had asked the other accusingly.

"They were there."

They had grimaced at each other and neither took responsibility for the perceived error- the blame had been hanging in the air waiting to settle. Flamboyant costumes, labelled and strung up on the overhead hanging rails, had resembled something like a psychedelic charity jumble sale. Faded patterned chairs were aligned around the room reminiscent of a therapy session, perhaps foretelling the futures of these girls. Each chair had been labelled with the names of the performers. They were close and touching- and the tension in the room had been tangible. I hadn't been able to deal with their nerves- I had little interest in their feelings- I had been trying to get a handle on my own.

The space had never been sufficient for the needs of all. Each girl vied for the best space- in front of the dressing room mirror had always been a favoured spot. Sought after. Nobody had wanted to sit by the costume boxes or the hanging rails- especially not me. I had needed space- a clear surface to place my essentials and organise myself: hair piece, eye pallet, slides, grips, Capezio tights, strapless bra. The list was endless. In life, I had already learned that I hadn't always get what I had needed. It hadn't meant that I ever accepted this graciously, though. Of course I hadn't. And my success at hiding my displeasure was at times below par. The mask sometimes slipped. A flicker of annoyance had crossed my face momentarily, when the realisation of where I was to sit had dawned on me. I had cursed my dad for dropping me to the theatre later than I would have liked. Early was always my preference- there was time to deal with things that might spontaneously present themselves. Being late was always a losing move- I hadn't time to organise and prepare or to get the seat I had so desperately wanted. But nobody else made a fuss so neither did I- my mask was on. Inside, I had burned with jealousy and irritation but having arrived with my stage make-up done already, there was no way I would have let tear streaks ruin my hard work. Instead I had planned ahead- I had become accustomed to meeting my own needs and I knew that tomorrow I would be at the dressing room first. I needed time to get myself organised without the other bodies crowding the small space.

Quietly, I had sat under the costumes, stuck in a corner- tassels were hanging down and had tickled my cold bare shoulders. People would no doubt think me abnormal for believing there had been money spiders crawling down my arm, but that is exactly what image had run through my head. I pushed the tassels away, annoyed. Worried. Anxious. As if this room hadn't been claustrophobic enough, my air space had been blocked with fabric- scratchy sequins and clinging Lycra. I had felt trapped. My sullenness in this situation had offended- yet it had been one of the ways that I had stopped myself from crying. Sulkiness or tears? I had chosen to present as the former- a proven coping mechanism. Possibly, I had been thought of as diva for wanting pole position. I was perceived as spoilt- a bitch even. I was not so socially inept that I hadn't been able to read the looks or notice the rolls of the eye from some. The truth of the matter had been that I was not overly bothered by their reactions: what they might have thought hadn't actually registered. It was what I thought that had mattered. Had I cared that they may have also wanted the space by the mirrors? Had I considered their feelings in any way? I had sat under the costumes, with the hanging tassels, not because I was considerate to the other girls. I had sat there because they had got to the mirrors first- those were the 'rules'. They had won. I had planned to beat them to the mirrors next show time and I wouldn't spare them a thought- although of course, I would pretend to.

Simmering inside, I had accepted my place- I had managed. Just. I might have read my book and chosen not to engage with the frolics and laughter. Lost in the pages, I had focused and tried hard to forget what was happening around me- I had zoned out from any judgments, the noise, the chatter....... I hadn't actually been sulking- I had been coping. I might have chosen to reapply my scarlet lipstick. Add more gloss. Build the mask up another layer. I had often thought that we looked like ghastly circus clowns with our thick foundation and painted smiles; the only difference was that my teardrop was invisible and not painted crudely on my cheek for all to see.

Just looking around the dressing room would have been a clue to the differences between my dance friends and I- if anyone had actually had the time to make comparisons. Whereas their belongings had been a chaotic form of order, mine were stacked and neatly ordered. I had a system- a structured and well rehearsed method. Each pair of shoes had been paired and neatly aligned up together. I had looked at how the other girls rushed in from stage, pulling their shoes off in haste and letting them remain where they fell. I had known that in a short while, a panic would begin where one of them would not be able to locate her silver heeled sandal. As much as I had copied, I had never copied their disorganisation. I wouldn't have ever got through a show if I had. My smooth, satin pointe shoe ribbons were folded neatly and the pink flesh ballet tights sat beneath them. The knickers, needed as under garments, were ordered in the sequence that they would be worn; the different bras needed for the varying costumes were stacked. To me, the chaperones were indispensable too- we had had the same few volunteer for years and I knew their system and they knew mine. Every time I had left the room for the stage, I had returned to my chair to find the next costume sitting their ready. Slick. Control, in a world of absolute madness. Just what I had needed and of course what I had needed was important to me.

Costume fitting had always been a challenging experience too, but I had watched and learnt. I had realised that it was polite to sit back and wait for my turn- even if my instinct was to rush in and claim the best fitting outfit. I hadn't always been able to control my natural urges and I worked damn hard to keep the poker face intact when I was given what I hadn't wanted to wear. I had stood expressionless, as if I was having an outer body experience, as the fitters had jabbed and squeezed me. Each touch had burned and made me recoil- but I tried hard not to flinch. My mask had been fully on.

"Face the window, please", one had requested, before hastily calling me back after I had walked over to the window to put my face towards it.

Of course, I hadn't wanted the costume with missing beads either- it was imperfect- threads were hanging down like convoluted angel hair. Why should I have had the flawed one? It had not even registered with me that neither should the other girls; as much as I had liked them (I really had) I had been indifferent to their feelings. But I had accepted what I had been given- that was the polite reaction after all- yet internally I had simmered with annoyance wearing my painted smile. I hadn't wanted the overly large outfit, or the outfit that was just that little bit too tight. Like Goldilocks, I had wanted what felt just right. I always have done- I guess it is no one's fault that this need remained hidden. It had taken my mother years until she had let me wear what I had wanted without a fight. Even from as early as I can recall, I had refused to wear denim. Not enough stretch, you see, too restrictive and rough.

"I will not be dictated to by a five-year-old! You will wear what I tell you to wear!" Mum had once exclaimed.

Except I hadn't. Jeans had been abandoned and I had identical velour tracksuits in six different colours; smooth to the touch and plenty of give. Mum had bought as many as she could find in that same style. Now I just wear as little as possible. Crop tops, the shortest shorts- I had always preferred the summer fashion and the lack of fabric which accompanied it. I had cared not if people disapproved- it was my body. Other's opinions had never really affected me, anyway.

In my dance setting, I knew exactly what to wear and had always done as I was told. I accepted, just like everyone else had. I had done my utmost best to ignore the tight strap cutting into my shoulder or the circular sequins scratching my underarms. The purple red marks and sores had been evidence of my discomfort, but I hadn't complained- nobody else had. Instead, I had cried when I got home; my stress and frustrations had attacked those I lived with. Upon entering the sanctuary of home, I had unleashed my pent-up emotions. I might have slammed the kitchen cupboards doors or deliberately started a row with my siblings. It had taken about half an hour for me to admit the real issue and my parents knew, despite my protestations of claiming 'I'm fine!", that I really was not. Far from fine. Lucky them- they had seen the best and absolute worst of me, whereas everyone else had seen only what I had allowed them to see.

At dancing, I had never allowed anybody to see me cry over a costume. I had sorted it- safety pins and cotton thread had made them fit. People might have noticed the additional safety pins holding me in- far more than possibly needed- but I had already watched the imaginary montage of images playing in my mind in which my costume pinged open live on stage. Just one of the stage fright scenarios I mentioned previously. Better to plan for disaster than to cope with the potential fallout and misery by being unprepared. No one had ever noticed the many pins though- I had forgotten sometimes that it was me who could always see the finer details. Ten safety pins when one would suffice. I had always ensured that I had brought many with me in my kit bag- enough for me and a few spare if anyone else had needed them. I had to know that I had enough and had felt reluctant to share at times- although of course I had done so. It would have been rude to decline such a request from friends. There was never anything I could do about an ill-fitting headdress though. Anxiously, I had selected one and had desperately forced it to mould to my head- gently bending the metal of the head cage so that it would fit like a snug helmet. I had felt smug that I hadn't been left with the larger one- even though I had known it would cause one of the girls discomfort- I had been grateful that the discomfort was not to be mine. There was nothing worse than performing an opening cabaret showstopper routine with a shaky headdress- it hurt and wobbled precariously. The levels of stress that I had felt were unfathomable at times- worried that it would fall, my dancing suffered in those particular numbers. Selfishly, it would have seemed, I had written my name on a label and fastened it tightly to the head frame. Perhaps labels could be handy after all? What's mine is mine. Hands off. I had known which was mine and which was theirs. I had taken note- of course I had.

Stealthily, I had watched them all- they were peers, friends, 'teachers'. I had learnt so much from my secret observations. In the midst of the dressing room chaos, I had decided not to get my breasts out any longer. There had been a time that I had walked around topless- I hadn't cared and it certainly hadn't concerned me about how it made others feel. We had done that since we were age 5 so why had it suddenly been an issue in our early teens? Why would I have worried- they were my breasts and not theirs? The other girls hadn't needed to look at me if they hadn't wanted to. However, I soon pretended that I had cared. A quiet whisper in my ear from one of the chaperones had been all that was needed for me to change course. An explicit comment had often been enough.

"Shall we get those covered?" they had gestured and made a sign towards my breasts.

"Why? I am going to switch outfits in a little while," I had replied.

"Yes, but put a bra on or cover up with your hoody whilst you are waiting- we don't want you to get cold," they had advised, kindly.

Though I hadn't been cold, I had done as requested. I had stopped sitting with my breasts out between costume changes. Instead, I had rushed from the stage back to the crowded dressing room and switched outfits immediately. There had been no more sitting around in just my Capezio tights and knickers. I had realised that this was not how things were done- even though it was easier to change costumes when I was not trying to protect my dignity. Trying to be modest by changing under a T-shirt- half contortionist half escapologist- had been one of the hardest things to do at speed. Yet that had been what everybody else had done, so I had followed suite. I had wished that I could have encouraged them all not to give a damn- that we were all girls together. Get your breasts out, get changed and be done- just like we had done when we were younger- but I guess I was the follower and not the leader then. If none of the girls had been free and liberal yet, despite the stress inducing quick changes, then neither would I have been. I had been slow not to observe the transition from child to pubescent teen and had simply carried on as we had always done. Clearly, 'new' teenagers covered up and I had missed this subtle change. So, I had watched and adapted again - I would certainly not let myself be seen to be different- not on the surface anyway.

Chpt 3: The role of 'The Collector'

I have had so many collections that I've lost count. Except I haven't of course- that is just a learned phrase that people say. I knew exactly what my collections consisted of and they have all depended on those around me. They had been driven by friends, acquaintances - I had become interested in something because they were interested. Their hobby had become my hobby. The difference though, was that mine had become a borderline obsession. A necessity.... a need. A life and death situation. There's another learned phrase for you.

My first collection had been lip balms. Well, I had had many before that one, but that was when I had been indulged by my parents in my infant years. I had loved Disney princesses and they had fed my every whim. They had seen what had provoked a positive reaction and had stuck with it. A winning formula. I'm sure most parents do the same when they have small children, to be fair.

However, the lip balm collection had been driven by my own will. I had never seen such an interesting lip balm until my friend had brought one back from the States- it had resembled a small egg. It opened with a gentle twist to reveal a perfect dome shape of waxy scent beneath. She had loved it and therefore so had I. I had wanted some- in fact I had wanted all of them- one in every colour/ scent. That is where my pocket money and birthday money had gone for six whole months. I hadn't used them - I hadn't wanted any of them to *actually* use. They weren't to be used: they had been bought just to be collected, to be counted, to be ordered in shade sequence - rainbow colours. Richard of York Gave Battle in Vain.

Their waxy domes had been left fingerprint and lip print free. And my siblings knew that I would notice the smudge on the otherwise glistening hub of wax if one of them had tried to use it. The lines of their forefinger would have been recorded in the wax- like a fossil in a rock. A fingerprint in a crime scene- I would have detected it. But I would have known before I had checked the balm itself, wouldn't I? Of course I would have. I would have noticed that the pots had moved rank, switched positions, abandoned order. My siblings wouldn't have recalled what sequence I had ordered them in, yet I would know at a glance that they had been touched. As I said, I have always noticed the small things.

I had moved on from lip balms to books. The move had been triggered by a friendship group shift and a new start at secondary school. The switch had been overwhelming – not that I would have allowed anyone to recognise my difficulties though. I had often thought fondly back to my junior school and my old teachers there. For me, change had never been a good experience.

"We'll always have the mirror maze," my primary teacher had signed in my leaving book.

This had been a throwback to our year 6 leaver's trip where it had been necessary for him to rescue and escort me screaming from the maze at a top London attraction. I had been the only child out of 90 who had behaved in that manner, but I had genuinely thought that I was trapped and that there was no escape. Every point I had turned had been a dead end- triangular shaped mirrors had reflected my fearful face to infinity. Screaming face, after screaming face, had bounced back and forwards across the glass…... Mum found out what had happened a year later when she had questioned me about the comment in my book- she hadn't read it previously. She had been tearful about the incident: why had no one told her? I hadn't understood why she had been so bothered. What had she been making a fuss about? It hadn't been her imprisoned had it? Seriously, what had she got to be so upset about?

I had later found solace in the new secondary school library and frequented it every lunchtime- without fail. No default. The serene space had been idyllic: people were spaced out amongst rows of organised books. The Dewy system screamed logic and order. Not too many people had ever been allowed in at one time- although I was always allowed in. There was a routine in there and structure- rules to adhere to. Hushed whispers. And so I had become a book lover and still am. This obsession was very much part of me. There was a time when I had carried a book everywhere with me- a comfort blanket. The holed cellular cot blanket had been replaced with a hard cover and graphics. If I had been feeling the pressure of life and had wondered what to do, what to say, how to cope- I had absorbed myself in a book. People hadn't interrupted me whilst I was reading. People hadn't thought me rude for ignoring them when I was reading; it was an acceptable antisocial activity. I had discovered the perfect disguise. As expected, I had made a few mistakes- sometimes, by error, I had allowed people to question what my book really represented; sometimes my prop would be seen for what it really was.

Once, I had arranged to see a film at the cinema with a dance friend. It had been back in the days when I had just started to go out a little with a trusted friend. Dad had always taken me and dropped me off- I had the entire itinerary planned- of course. Everyone had always thought that Dad was so great dropping and collecting me and whichever friends I had been with. The reality was that there was no way I would have gone on my own. Dad had taken me and used to wait until I had company. It was the same collecting me- I hadn't wanted to be the last one standing, so Dad had always been there earlier than I had needed him.

One particular time, my friend had been with us at home. We left to get in the car and suddenly, I had yelled that I needed to go back in the house.

"I need to get my book! I have forgotten it!" I had said in anguish.

My friend had laughed when I ran back into the house to get it. "What do you want your book for? You can't read in the dark!" she had giggled kindly.

I had laughed, too. Stupid me. It was easier to play the dumb role, the ditsy one sometimes- I would go far to keep my deception. I had taken my book anyway- I read it whilst queueing. It had taken my mind off the many people there.

My parents had become very concerned- I had been reading for hours each day -but I had received so many books for Christmas (indulging my whims again!) and I had felt that I needed to 'get through' them. 'Needed to'- that was where the obsession part had happened. It hadn't been that I needed to- I felt that I *had* to. The bookshelf in my room had been bowing under the pressure of the books which were double stacked on it. I had tried colour organising them and then by size or thickness. Neither had looked quite right and I felt stressed- under pressure. I hadn't wanted to have books on my shelf that weren't read- they were increasing in number and I felt panicked seeing them on the shelf. It sounded irrational, but what was the point of having unread books? They weren't ornaments. The whole purpose of a book was to read it. Painstakingly, I planned what to read and in what sequence. I wrote a list. I wrote several, in fact. I tried to invent my own Dewy system. That way I had an order to my reading. No book would be left out. My parents had already learnt not to buy too many in one hit- otherwise they hadn't seen see me for days; I had been found in bed, snuggled under an arrangement of soft fleeces. Sometimes I had woken up super early or read extremely late into the night or early hours, feeling exhausted the next day because of it. My head had pounded and my eyes were dull and heavy- it was actually making me ill, but I couldn't stop as I had pages to get through. Mum had eventually showed be some novels that she had bought 18 months previously- they were still unread. I got it. It was okay not to read every book that I had owned. I understood: the secret and twilight reading ended.

I had soon learned to stay away from book sets; a self-preservation. Otherwise, I had read the first, and then I had wanted to read them all. My mood had been terrible- agitation had set in and real drama occurred if a collection was incomplete. I guess amazon and eBay helped. I had searched for hours looking for the missing link to a collection. The way I felt reminded me of a film I had seen- where three witches were searching for a beetle. They pulled the entire house apart searching for it- desperate. Panicked. They had to locate it. That is how I had felt, too. It was just frustrating if the missing book arrived and it hadn't had the same style jacket- it messed up the order of what it looked like on the shelf. Feng shui, another learned phrase, or that is what I had claimed. It was this very same reason why my bed had about 15 plump cushions organised daily on them- it was aesthetically pleasing, calming for my soul. How things were arranged and looked were always important to me.

My book preoccupation then moved over to make-up, which had been my most costly obsession. I can take it or leave it now. At the time though, I had watched the older girls in the dance dressing room. I watched as they cooed over a mascara and showed great delight in a lip gloss. They moved the loaded wand slickly across their plump lips in an elaborate gesture to prove how wonderful the product was.

"Where's that from? How much?" I would interrupt.

I had listened and taken note. I would be on Amazon later- fact. Their make-up bags had split open like burst treasure chests- glass, colours and plastic dazzled in the spotlights. I had watched their excitement and soon I had also been displaying the same levels of ecstasy over an eye shadow pallet. Except I had several- one in each set of hues, all of which I never wore. Sets of creams, greens, browns and purple - with accompanying brushes. They had been stashed in size order in my dressing table drawer: I hadn't bought them to wear them, had I?

I had tried to be the same as them; my chameleon changing colours were out in force. I joined in their conversations and admired their goods. I demanded dearer makeup at home- I hadn't wanted the cheap brands anymore because nobody else had used those brands. I trawled online looking at makeup tutorials- because that is what they did. Much to my parents' dismay, I spent my birthday money on a 'designer' lip gloss- £28. I adored the little bag it came in and would polish the silver lid so that it was smudge free. It shone like a small rectangular mirror and complimented the glittery pastel pink gloss perfectly.

Suddenly, I had known all about contouring and what oil products would lengthen my lashes. I had concealed my copycat mannerisms. I was interested in makeup because they were. Simple as that. Other friends did try to convince me that I hadn't needed to wear full makeup to go to school.... but the obsession had taken a firm grip by then. I lied and maintained that I enjoyed wearing it all the time. It had become a situation where I had to wear a full make up face. I needed the painted mask. The little zipped bag full of precious jewels accompanied me to school- it was as important to me as the 'school bag'. I had panicked some school mornings when I had been made to leave the house and the makeup hadn't been quite done. I had sat moodily in the car and touched up the face every time the car slowed- my hands had been shaky with the engine's murmuring vibrations. The expletives would hang in the air like punches when my unsteady hand made a mistake. The painted clown again- but this time not such garish colours. No one wore blue eyeshadow to school, did they?

I had so many more collections that I could share…… If each were looked at as a separate case, then they probably were insignificant. When considered collectively, a pattern might just emerge. The obsession, the fear and stress, the painstaking time invested might have been noticed. I had been a magpie- I hadn't stolen the silver, but other people's interests sparkled and glittered enough for me to want to replicate them. And of course, I had taken that interest one step further- another level. Every time.

Chpt 4 : The role of 'The daughter'

Unsurprisingly, I had been fairly tricky to live with at points in my life. I obviously hadn't thought that at the time, but I have been told enough times since. It had actually been quite helpful to hear about my 'funny little ways'. I never hid myself at home. At home- I had been the most 'me' that would ever be seen. A bitch at times- once I had been called a 'spoilt creature' by my mum. I had sobbed relentlessly. She found me on the stairs with me head in my hands, my eyes swollen and red with incessant crying. I was evidently distraught. I wasn't a creature; I wasn't an insect. Mum apologised and explained what she had actually meant. I had pretended to understand, but why call me that if it hadn't been meant though? It was quite obvious I hadn't six legs and a segmented body. I guess people would have expected me to have known better at age 14, but comments like that still threw me. I struggled to process meaning then. Other people's metaphorical language confused me; although my own ability to use language had never caused me a problem, I hadn't always got what other people meant. I had been in control of my own language and had imagined my own comparisons whereas at times, I was dumfounded by the imagery and comparisons of others.

Maybe I had been spoilt – people might have thought that about me if they hadn't understood me- luckily, my parents got it, most of the time. They had 'got it' late mind, I won't be giving them any medal for observance here. Mum had realised I had been somewhere on the spectrum having spoken to a specialist SEN teacher at her work. I think she had literally recounted all my quirks like a therapy session, and then the penny had dropped. Then the guilt. How had she not seen? How had she not connected the dots? I was just a girl and girls got anxious, right? Girls get moody, hormonal. Shy. Time of the month. Relationship issues. Girls all like the same things. Girls collect things. Wasn't that how it went? Or still does? Only boys are Autistic, right?

Apparently, I had always been a little.... quirky, shall I say? Odd? They had thought that I would 'grow out of it'- that my behaviours had been a 'stage'. Except I hadn't grown out of my ways but had managed the best I could with coping. When I had reached double digits, mum was beginning to wonder why I was still doing things that hadn't really been appropriate for my age. My actions, she had believed, were not age appropriate or even ability appropriate; I was a bright and able child so why had I still not been picking up on other's social cues and language?

Once, as he often did, Dad had been ranting in the car. Rain was pounding the windscreen and rivers of raindrops were racing down the screen. The wipers were thrashing back and forth, and I had winced at the sound.

"I can't see Jack shit, here!" he had exclaimed angrily.

"Why do you want to see Jack Shit?" I had queried.

As a small child, Mum had often told everybody that I was 'tired' if I behaved in way that was even slightly embarrassing. If I had suddenly been moody or had a full out sulk or tantrum it had been 'tiredness'- nothing an early night wouldn't have remedied. There had been a time when relations with the in-laws had become a little strained, as nobody had seen me like I was when at home. Going out for evening meals became a stressful situation. My parents had stopped accepting invitations out- much to the dismay and annoyance of the family. Mum has since told me that she had declined to take me places, as she had just known that I was more settled and happier at home. Life was easier at home. Parties and big family occasions had caused stress- particularly upon leaving and getting home. Dad had said that I had a witching hour at 6pm- if I hadn't been in the bath and doing the 'wind down' bedtime routine at that time, it would have been guaranteed that I hadn't settled that night. They had said that on some evenings where we had gone out, they would have to do the whole routine at 10pm at night, upon return home. It had been as though I knew that we had missed a step and that step needed to happen to get me back in sync. Of course, everyone had offered their advice and criticism. Mum and Dad had used to make excuses and say they had plans when in fact they hadn't. They just wanted a calmer, hassle free day at home with me in my own environment. No judgement or explanations needed.

I had never been a settled baby and mum went back to work when I was four months- she was glad to but already exhausted. She later thought this had damaged me slightly - but no. I had later wondered if she might have picked up on my needs sooner had she been with me more but it hadn't been her fault. Work commitments and all that. She had shared me with nursery and my two grandmas- of which neither had ever said anything was amiss. I was the first grandchild and was loved unconditionally.

Nursery had nearly refused to have me though. Mum had told me the story of my first sessions, age two, when I vomited every time she had dropped me off. She had said that I knew where I was the minute the car stopped outside the nursery and I had then screamed so much and kicked that I had actually been sick. Nursery had said it could not continue and that I might not be able to keep the place as I just hadn't settled. I had been a large toddler and maybe harder to manage than the smaller more subservient children. However, I had stopped doing it short of two weeks. Vomiting and stress had started again when I changed floors a year later and had been issued a new keyperson, but a sticker chart and explicit rules had kept me in check. They had also organised a short 6-month stint with a speech therapist after setting observations of me. More rules to follow. Easy. Simple. Even at that young age I had clearly liked simple structure and order and was becoming more able to follow them.

My parents admitted that they had just thought I was a difficult child- moody sometimes, loving many a time. They had learnt to cope with me by accident, I guess. If I hadn't eaten pasta in red sauce, I was then not given it. Ever. I hadn't even been able to explain why I hadn't liked it at the time. I ate poached salmon nearly every night for two weeks because it was my favourite, apparently. I ate it so they fed me it: 'fussy eater' became my new label. I consumed Shreddies for breakfast every day but one day refused them. I hadn't eaten baked beans- but many kids hadn't. They bribed me once with a pecan pie to encourage me to eat what was on my plate.

"Eat the beans or the pie goes in the bin," Dad had said in simple language.

I had refused. The pie had been discarded in the bin. All hell had broken loose I have been told; I really lost my control: apparently- hyperventilating, screaming, lashing out and thrashing my arms. I had done that quite often when I hadn't got my own way. Funny thing is, I love beans now but only if they are piping hot, thick not runny and are of a certain brand.

In my teenage years, I had always been a little odd with food too. Meals had been an 'occasion'- I sat like a princess and ate slowly and precisely. Take pizza- the siblings had just eaten out of the box, greasy fingers and mouths. I had ensured I had eaten mine like I had been visiting a Michelin star restaurant. Plate, knife and fork. Just the crisp white linen and crystal glass was missing. Last one to finish. I could be put off a meal by a smell or look- most of my food had to be arranged aesthetically on the plate. Mum knew I wouldn't have eaten it otherwise. God help her too if she had changed her mind on what she had planned for dinner. If I had not been prepared for the meal, I had refused to eat it. I had often asked in the morning what dinner would be and if it by dinner time I was served something else- I would break down. Fortunately, she had soon realised that and either hadn't committed to naming a choice or had stuck religiously to what was said. Cue sulks and tears, otherwise. Age 15, I had actually cried: instead of having pancakes that had been promised, Mum had made a sausage casserole. My siblings had sat at the table devouring fluffy potato and meaty gravy. The littlest one was struggling to cut her sausages, but I had just stared at her with utter contempt. Why weren't any of them angry like me? My own plate remained untouched. I had threatened not to eat anything- that I would sooner starve.....But who wouldn't have wanted pancakes over sausages? I had been imagining having them all day; I was looking forward to them. I had been convinced that I had a fair point and that Mum had lied- she had said we were having pancakes. I usually am right as far as I am concerned.

Yet, if I had been at a friend's house, I would have eaten whatever was given to me. It would have been rude not to. If the host family ate pizza out of the box, I certainly wouldn't have asked for a knife and fork. The chameleon changed shade yet again, the painted face primed.

Habits and routines had been very much part of my life when I was younger. My parents permitted me to have my dummy until I was 4+, because I hadn't sleep without it. With both of them working and a third baby on the way- I guess it had been sheer desperation rather than just giving in to my childhood demands. The vomiting had started at bedtime when they had tried to take my dummy away- I guess there was only so much of that which they could withstand until they had given in. There had been no sleep for them: changing bedsheets every night and the floor stinking of cheese due to milky vomit. I had my carpet changed at a cost and the dummy stayed. Spoilt, right? Over indulged? Bad parenting? Parental survival?

I 'had' to watch the same Disney movie every night before bath time, but my parents had blamed themselves for 'accidental parenting'; when a parent slipped into a routine by accident and then could not break the habit that they had created. Mum had read the manuals- how to have a sleeping baby by 4 months etc etc.... Weaning guides- the lot. Seemingly, the tips and advice had worked a treat on all my subsequent siblings. I had obviously been immune to their efforts- one size clearly certainly hadn't fitted all. Where had they gone wrong? If I hadn't been the first child and them 'new' parents, might their concerns have actually been listened to instead of dismissed?

So, Princess Aurora it was- Sleeping Beauty became part of the family. One of my first phrases had been "I know, I know" which I said incessantly, but nobody had a clue what it meant other than family. "I know you, I've danced with you once upon a dream," except I hadn't been able to say the whole sentence. I had even been bought a bear for my second birthday that had this phrase added to the stuffing in a voice box. It had remained as my bed companion well into my teens.

Every night, I had resisted going upstairs until the cartoon film had been watched. So, a routine had been born. Dinner, film, bath, book and milk- in a bottle- even when I was three/four. I hadn't settled until I had slurped warm milk from the same style bottle that I had from birth. I also had my birth cot blanket- a cellular soft wool style- that I had taken everywhere with me. It was no longer the fresh yellow that it once had been and had developed a greyish tinge to it- but it had felt the same. I had been distraught when it had ripped in the car door and I rejected it after it had been stitched up. The new cotton stitches had felt rough and sharp even. Mothercare had stopped selling it and my Nanny had been tasked with trawling the second-hand shops in town to find a replacement. One had been found and I was successfully deceived; it had felt exactly the same- soft with the pattern of cellular holes and satin shiny smooth ribbon bordering each side. When the label had fallen off another one had been sewn on- I used to tickle my nose with it and when I had discovered it had disappeared from my blanket, sleep was not ever going to happen until it had been replaced.

I hadn't slept well then and I am a bit inconsistent in that area even now. My mum had often slept on the floor next to my bed many a time when I was younger, but again, so many parents resort to desperate measures to get sleep. She'd had two more children by then and they hadn't been like me- they were 'textbook'. She had blamed herself for being a first-time mother and to be fair, I think others had to. She had told me the doctors and health professionals had often said, "Is this your first child?" whenever she had raised concerns.

I had tried so many different beds. It hadn't been me you see- it must have been the wrong type of bed. The traditional cot had been abandoned after a year as I had been caught trying to escape from it.

The worry had been that I would actually manage-being large for my age- and that I would have fallen to the floor, hurt. A toddler bed, mid sleeper, single divan.... I had experienced them all by a very young age but had still felt that green pea. A princess through and through. By my early teens, I had been bought a double bed and sleep was getting easier to achieve. (So long as I had the correct fabric bed sheets and a window open.) If I had been having a 'moment' I had chosen to sleep on the floor in my parents' room- even at age 15. People might think that really weird, but my parents never objected- they knew that I would have only wanted to if I had needed settling and calming down- comfort and parental presence. Perhaps they had worried that I would have done something silly if I had been left on my own. Cut myself? Silly them. Why would I have done that and left ugly scars on my wrists? Sometimes, I had even lain in the bed next to my mum for a bit too- I was never too old for that. I found it calming and relaxing and had often read my book before feeling sleepy. The fact I was taller and stronger than her meant I took up space but that was what they bought a king size bed for. I had known it hadn't been for my six-year-old sibling. She had never experienced difficulty with sleeping on her own.

I think they had realised they were not 'bad parents' by the time they had child number 4. My three siblings were totally what the manuals had said. Good eaters, sleepers, potty trained, dummies removed at a year....happy and contented. So had I been, but just perhaps not in the same way.

Chapter 5: The role of 'The Dreamer'

What are dreams? Are they snapshot images of what might happen in our futures- do we control our subconscious and re-enact our fears or desires? As one might guess, I had often dreamed a lot. I daydreamed too. I imagined all sorts of things happening and my mind was like Netflix- so many screenplays to choose and relive. Over and over.

I would take a seed and allow it to grow. An innocent or flippant thing that might have been said would take a hold and root deep inside of me; the sprout would bend upwards and the leaves unfurl. Like a weed, it would secure its patch and grow night and day; it multiplied until there was not enough of me left to rationalise with it. I lost so many times. The patch of earth was overrun.

Fire had always been something that terrified me. The intense orange flames , which licked, curled and flicked in the air - filled me with absolute dread. I had dreamt of fire; I ran from fire no matter how large or small. Every year, on my birthday, I had found the birthday cake an ordeal. Cringing, I had backed away from my birthday cake due to the candles. The family had all thought sweetly of me, that I had been embarrassed or nervous in front of everyone singing. The family assumed I hadn't liked being the centre of attention. What they hadn't understand was that even watching the candles being lit filled me with fear.

"Ouch, shit SHIT!" Dad cursed as he had misjudged the matchstick and nearly burnt his fingers. The flame ate up the short wooden splint and nearly touched his fingertips. He had lit another and held it expectantly over the candle wick. Two previously lit candles had blown out and the charade began again. It had been like a race- would the wick catch alight before the matchstick burnt itself out? I hadn't been able to stand the stress and had looked away.

I had stood fidgety and awkward- the guests all smiled encouragingly. Tentatively, I blew and backed away, blew and backed away. Every damn year there had been even more candles. There had practically been an inferno on fondant! My mum winked- she knew, but the rest of the guests had suspected nothing. I had allowed the younger cousins to help me extinguish the taunting flames- they had excitedly obliged and my fear had remained undetected in the most part. I had suddenly been the kind cousin who had shared the birthday cake candle blowing- wasn't that lovely of me right? What a kind girl I had been…. Now I had spit and germs on my cake- don't think I hadn't noticed the spittle as they blew.

Actually, I had liked birthdays. I knew how to behave at birthday gatherings; I had been to enough parties and family events to learn and replicate the rules. I wore a nice outfit; I greeted the guests and I thanked them for 'my lovely presents'. I was learning all the time. 'That's so kind of you…ah you really didn't need to get me that.' Learned phrases- I swept them up and stored them in my head. Each one had been labelled and put on a shelf for later- it was useful to keep stocked up as I never knew when I would be caught short or left hanging whilst an awkward silence ensued. Did I ever mean them- sometimes and sometimes not? Do you always mean what you say? Am I that different, really?

My fear of fire hadn't just stopped at candles. School fire alarms had been a horrendous ordeal and I think if there had been a real fire, I would have been the one hiding in a cupboard; too afraid of the actual fire itself to actually run from it. I had heard that this happens; I had read the news. Young siblings found huddled together under the bed, suffocated by the smoke. The older one embraces the youngest, her soft blonde curls resting lightly on her older brother's shoulders. His eyes are wide and expressionless. The mother weeps outside on the lawn. If only she hadn't left the plug sockets on. I had played this in my mind plenty of times. Sometimes they were under the bed- other times they were found just by the back door- so close to being saved. I imagined they were my own siblings and wept. This probably sounds irrational, but it was the way my mind ticked. I could invent a sequel or prequel even. I was the scriptwriter and director…and the audience. Even the critic.

I had learned not to scream and cry when an alarm went off- I knew that most of the time it had been just a drill- a practice, a pretence. I understood what a pretence meant, and I had learnt to just follow in a line as everyone else left the building. I had experienced the training from the fire service when they delivered their presentation about fire safety at primary school. I hadn't watched the last bit though- where they had replayed a real telephone call of a desperate parent whose child was trapped in a blaze- I was crying without restraint and had been removed from the school hall at that point. I had learnt enough though. There were rules to obey when the alarms went off and I could do that. Keep the mask intact. Rules were totally my thing. Stop, drop and roll.

Nightmares and sleep walking used to occur at times but not so frequently as I became older. Friends might have laughed and mocked me at a sleepover. Had I really caused such amusement when I started babbling away in sleep mode? Film me if they liked- I hadn't cared that much. They had laughed- so I must have been funny, right? I was the painted clown after all- I could be the comedian and be the fool if that had been what was wanted. I had laughed too, when they had showed me in the morning. Hilarious, wasn't it? Maybe I wouldn't stay over next time, though. Maybe I had plans...... Maybe they hadn't noticed that I wasn't laughing on the inside. Maybe they hadn't cared?

I had never been certain as to what triggered a nightmare. I think it had probably been a film that I had played in my mind before I fell asleep- one where I had forgotten to press the pause button. The basic tumble dryer had given me nightmares for weeks. I had seen an advert on TV about a faulty dryer made by the same company as ours. Black dense smoke had been billowing out of it like giants and the plastic had melted like wax. I had been convinced that ours would suffer the same fate so every time it was put on, I had swiftly turned it off. Stealth like of course. Mum had thought there had been something wrong with it- couldn't fathom out why it kept cutting out mid cycle. I had kept quiet and was smugly relieved. It was only when I had switched it off from the plug socket that she knew someone had touched it......

I had a habit of doing this though. It wasn't OCD; I just hadn't wanted the house to burn down whilst we were asleep. Don't think me irrational- it has happened. It was common sense, really. My parents had sometimes caught me creeping around attempting to turn all the wall sockets off, but I tried to do it without drawing too much attention to myself. They looked so much better with the switches pressed downwards- the red part of the switch tucked in. Tidier, somehow.

I had never considered what I turned off though, and that is where I had made mistakes. I recall a puddle of water was seeping from under the freezer; my mum was mopping it up wondering what had happened. She had twisted and turned the damp cloth that she was soaking the melt water with, cursing her appliance. She had opened the doors and drawers to check if the frozen goods had been spoiled. A finger jabbed at the meat and she tutted as she felt the softness of flesh; what she had wanted to feel was hard ice.

"Bloody freezer. Looks like we'll be eating this tonight," she had said irritably. "God know what's wrong with this damn thing- not even a year old…."

I had known of course; I turned around and walked back upstairs. She would find out soon enough wouldn't she?

On another occasion, the baby monitor had shrieked in the darkness - a frightening banshee wailed in the dead of night. Footsteps had resounded on the laminate flooring and my baby brother's door had been pushed open in panic.

"Ah, he's fine," Mum whispered, "Settle down sweetheart, snuggle up."

She pulled his blankets around his shoulders and gently stroked his forehead. She had always used to panic about him- his silent reflux issues caused her to worry as milk just sat in his oesophagus rather than erupting out of his mouth, potentially causing him to choke or suffocate. He had been under the consultant at the hospital and had special medicine which helped his food be digested quickly. His sensory sleep mat monitor wailed if it stopped detecting his movement…. Or if it was turned off at the wall socket and the backup battery expired. Had I ever turned it off? Yes- but with good reason. I had explained to my parents that the red light of the monitor looked like the colour of fire and that it needed turning off. It was a glowing angry flame in the blackest of night- it was unsafe to be left on. My parents' faces were angry looking, and their voices were different: I understood then that I must not touch it again. Reluctantly, I had obeyed.

Later, I had heard mum mutter about the school fire safety talk and vowed that she would 'have words' with my school about whether I would attend these things in the future.

If the baby monitor had been out of bounds, I had done other home safety checks instead. I had tampered with the central heating button. I had switched it off so that the red light, which had looked like a glowing lump of coal, faded away to a dull orange plastic rectangle. I was always too hot anyway. Of course, I hadn't questioned how the rest of the family would have felt waking up with no heating in the bedrooms. Would they have been cold? Had I even cared? I pretended not to hear the shrieks from the shower in the morning. Cold showers were supposed to be invigorating anyway.

I had progressed from a fear of fire to a fear of invasion. Our second family home was a bungalow which had brought challenges along the way too. My bedroom window remained closed as I suspected that someone could easily have climbed in whilst I had been sleeping. Ground floors bring those risks, don't they? I could imagine the blinds being parted and a soft training shoe, followed by a leg and then a body clambering through. They leave light footprints on the soft carpet but not a sound is otherwise made. My dresser drawers slide open silently and hands rummage through my lip balm collection. Lids are unscrewed and colours rearranged. My eye palettes are rifled through until my bracelets and charm collections are discovered. They hold cold silver in their dirty palm, calculating worth. I envisaged the intruder standing over me watching me sleep......I looked peaceful. My eyes flickered momentarily, and my mouth emitted a shallow breathing noise. There are so many different endings that played through my mind. I had woken up, I hadn't woken up, I got hurt: I played them on repeat in my mind. It had been fine though- I had coped with this dream because I was prepared. The early bird catches the worm.....well that was not the right idiom but I had always confused them. Anyway, every night, I had placed a wooden broom under the back-door handle to prevent any one breaking in. It hadn't mattered that there were already 7 deadlocks on the new UPVC door- the broom would make lock number eight. No chance of entering with the broom guarding the door, right? I had been satisfied that at least one door was blockaded. I had taken my chances with the other doors-I only had one broom, after all.

I had never liked toilet cubicles either. A ferry trip to France triggered that fear. It had been ridiculously choppy, and I was feeling so nauseous. My mother and I went to the toilets and the cubicle doors were slamming and opening- banging shut and then swinging open again. Here comes the chopper to chop of your head. Bang, slam, bang, slam. You're dead. My self-control had really slipped that day.

"Get me out! Get me out! The boat is sinking- it's sinking!" I had yelled in absolute panic.

 Mum had been changing a nappy and could not do anything to calm me down. Her hands were full- literally. I had tried to get out of the space, but in my panic, I must have been pushing the door the wrong way. More screaming had followed. I had raced around the toilet block pushing and pressing walls to see if there had been an alternative exit...a secret door. Anything. I had quite an audience when we had finally emerged from the toilet block onto the inner deck. I hadn't realised that they were there because of me though. I hadn't realised that they had all heard the commotion and were wondering what the hell was going on. I had just walked out amongst the congregating onlookers as if there was nothing wrong-as soon as I had managed to get the door open and exit, I had been absolutely calm. If I had known they were my audience, I would have curtseyed.

That had been where my fear of confined spaces started, I think. I hadn't easily used a lift, although when with friends I would often force myself. The mask was on then, and the painted smile would grin widely back at me in the lift mirror. It had been too wide to be genuine, if people had but looked more attentively. It had depended on the type of lift to whether I would be prepared to put myself through that ordeal. If it had been large and had mirrors- I could just about do it. If it was small and essentially a metal coffin, then I had pretended to need the exercise. In a metal lift there would have been no escape in a fire- yet with mirrors, there would be more chance of survival. Mirrors in a lift reminded me of windows- windows could be escaped through- it was logical and made perfect sense to me. Small lifts were not large enough for several people either; I worried the cable would snap and we would all hurtle to the floor. Instead, I had raced friends up the stairs sooner than take a lift.

I had been known to make my youngest sister walk up the 192 steps from the underground rather than step one foot in the lift there. Trains were the same. I have stood on the platform many times and allowed two trains to go past before I had been forced on one by my parents. I have made the whole family traipse across London on foot rather than get on a tube. The six-year-old had been easier to placate with walking, than I had been with embarking on a crowded train journey.

"You should have left me behind then if I'm causing a problem. I didn't want to come anyway." I had said spitefully.

Often, I had become nasty when feeling under pressure. In history, I had been told a story about Vladimir Putin and a rat. He had a wild rat backed in a corner once, at his poverty-stricken house as a child, and was surprised that it lunged up ferociously and attacked him. It was said that he learnt then, that if you back someone into a corner, making them desperate- they will attack. I was sometimes that rat.

As my dancing had progressed, it had become necessary for me to attend monthly sessions in south west London. To manage these journeys, we had planned our days around rush hour avoidance. I couldn't cope with standing on a packed train. People I hadn't known stood too close. I could smell their scents or their stale body odour. Hamsters. Onion. Bad breath. I was so close that I could see stained teeth and plaque. Nostril hair that needed cutting; white roots that needed a hairdresser sharpish. Why had I always noticed everything? Sweaty hands were too close to mine on the central pole. I had felt thighs and legs pushed up against mine, muscles flexed as they tried to keep a balance. So, I had zoned out; I had listened to the rattling of the carriages- I deep breathed- some might call it hyperventilating, or close to it. I had closed my eyes and counted: 5,6,7,8. I had been given strange looks, but had I cared? What people hadn't realised was that if it had been possible for me to jump off the claustrophobic nightmare I would have. I had planned my escape in my head. I looked left and right and behind me. The next station had been approaching- the doors would open and people would soon disembark. My face must have been giving my thoughts away. Dad had repositioned himself and stood by the doors just in case. Mum had smiled sympathetically whilst my siblings laughed and teased each other, oblivious to my terror. I really hadn't comprehended how they had managed these journeys. My six-year-old sister's face was at the same height as most people's hot crotch and my brother's face had been in the armpits of those holding the overhead poles. Vile. The smell and the imagined germs there, which multiplied in that warm environment, had made me want to throw up. What if these people hadn't washed? Some had certainly looked like they hadn't. Were they wearing clean underwear even? I had pressed the imaginary pause button in my mind as I hadn't wanted to visualise anymore. There must have been something wrong with my siblings, surely? Why could they stand so calmly as if being this close to strangers was normal?

Chpt 6 The role of 'The friend'

Had I been a decent friend? Had I been nice? Had people actually liked me or just tolerated me? I have never really been sure to be honest; I know I have had my rejections in the past or was that because I pushed them away without realising? I had once been told I was 'too intense' and subsequently 'unfriended', but my mum had seemed more bothered about that than I had been. With little care or reaction, I had simply found a new group of friends who liked to frequent the library during recreation time too. My sociability varied- sometimes I had wanted to chat for ages with friends. At other times, I would ignore the calls. Decline. Number busy. Phone was well and truly off.

"Sorry, I can't take your call right now- leave a message and I will get back to you."

Except I hadn't. I had no intention of returning those calls.

At times, I had just followed and taken the lead of my friends. I would be on the periphery and just fade into the background. At other times, I had wanted to forge my own path and do what suited me. Compromise hadn't always been easy.   Stubbornness? Bossiness? My way or the highway; or I would take my friend's way and simmer all day about it. I had often begrudged the fact that I had conceded and then resent them for the rest of the day- probably spitting venom about them when I got home- unable to mask my feelings any longer. But I tried hard not to show them my annoyance, as I was learning that it was not their fault necessarily.

I suppose that I did have Jekyll and Hyde characteristics. There was certainly a duplicity about me- I have recognised that much. There had been a valid reason why I hadn't liked to mix my dance friends and school friends together. I had claimed it was because *they* didn't mix, but it was more than that. I had been a different person depending on which group I had been with. Performance time. Which mask was I wearing? Jazz hands and all that.

Unlike Jejyll and Hyde- I hadn't thought that one of my 'faces' won over the other. And actually- neither of my personas had been evil. Not on the surface anyway. I wouldn't have dreamt of smashing my friend with a stick or trampling over their bruised body. I would have been arrested wouldn't I- that would have been breaking the law, right?

With my dance friends, life was exhilarating. I had been in the troupe for ten years and we had so many experiences together in our dance school and beyond. It had been their influence that had taught me to turn take, to be modest with my body, to share, to pout, to laugh and cry. I had grown up with them and had trusted them explicitly. Some of my friends got me totally. Others had still been a little unsure by my responses. One of them had teased me once and said there had been a spider on my shoulder in class- except I hadn't realised they were teasing. My reaction had not been what was obviously expected- I had cried. I had made a fuss. I had probably screamed. They had looked at me in abject horror and more so when the dance teacher had chastised them. Who cried about spiders at the age of 13? Especially when it had been a joke- I knew after, that absolutely no harm was meant, but at the time I had believed them wholly. Gullible? A tendency to take things literally? Absolutely.

They had been quite cross that I hadn't taken the joke as it had been intended. My friend looked horrified- confused at my hyperbolic response. Next time, I vowed that I would know what to do- I should have known to keep the emotions boxed in. I usually had. This one time though, I had let everyone see me as I was- my raw state of panic visible. The mask had been obliterated, and I had wondered if would ever be able to rebuild it: would I save face? I had vowed not be so open next time. I had logged my reaction and recorded the response for the future.

There was a reason why I had later developed a catch phrase: 'Is it actually?' It gave the person I was talking to a chance to clarify or readdress. It gave me time to process and evaluate the situation. Mum had picked up on it- but no one else had yet- I hadn't thought. I started saying it to check that I was understanding the situations I found myself in. Now I say it far too many times.
"Is it actually?" I had questioned.
"No- I'm joking!" one might say. Or they might confirm with, "Yeah- unbelievable isn't it?"
See how those three little words might save me? Is it actually? The phrase had been my lifeline- a chance to shift my thoughts quickly, a chance to change colour- to blend in without causing a commotion.

With genuine gratitude and feelings of contentment, I have had many 'first' experiences with my dance troupe. My first spa and sauna felt very adult- we took so many pictures it was ridiculous. I had posed like an Instagram model in my bikini- or that was what I thought I had been doing. My teenage breasts pushed up and outwards and my stomach sucked in- just like I had seen on screen. I uploaded to social media like my friends had….. A worried aunt had contacted my mum and the conversation about internet safety ensued. I posted images still- but not semi naked ones anymore. I have already said that I followed the rules- I had just needed to know what the rules were in the first place.

Fashion and styling had been something I had learned from all my friends. I loved their outfits and style- I had used the same internet shopping sites as them. Obviously. When I had seen something they had worn, I had tried hard to buy something similar. Or identical. At one time, some of the dance troupe had attended a dance weekend away. We had talked outfits and planned our suitcases meticulously. Velour tracksuits had definitely been a thing of the past by then- and anyway, none of my friends wore them so why would I have? My closest dance friend had arrived at the hotel door to meet me for dinner, dressed in crisp white jeans and a gingham top. She looked amazing. I hadn't been ready, so had nipped into the toilets with my clothes to get changed. Five minutes later, I emerged. I was also wearing crisp white jeans and a gingham top. Snap. Copycat. Don't know what you're looking at. My friend had blinked and looked down.

"I think you should wear your skirt," mum had said.

 "But I want to wear this."

"You can't, as your friend is wearing that," she had explained. She looked at my friend and winked. "You cannot go out wearing matching outfits- you're not on stage now!" she had said light heartedly.

She thought that I had never noticed her winks. Of course I had. I had taken them as a sign that I had done something I shouldn't have done. I really hadn't understood though. Mum and my Aunty used to buy my cousin and I matching outfits all the time. They had always said we looked cute in matching 'get ups'. I had all the photos- matching tutus, holiday outfits, wedding outfits .... shoes. Granted, we had been younger than age 14, but I had the photos to prove it still. We used to wear the same and purposely had shopping trips together so that the same outfits were purchased. At what age wasn't that to be permitted or to be encouraged anymore? No one had told me. My friend had been relieved when I changed. I had felt an idiot, stupid, embarrassed- but we laughed about it. She had always understood me totally and never judged. Even back in the dressing room, when I had offered to do her bun, she had said that I would probably want to put my bra on first.

"You wear it tomorrow" she said. "The top looked great."

"Did it actually?"

I had loved all of my friends, but I was certainly different with the two groups. I used to struggle, as I would gravitate between the two-swinging like a pendulum- sometimes feeling false, or out of rhythm and yet at other times feeling like my truest self. I had worn a mask for so long that even I had wondered who I was at times.

Chpt 7: The role of 'The Student'

I had been irritable, moody, monosyllabic in my responses to mum. My face had looked like a cracked pie, broken round the edges and no egg glazing to make it look pleasant.

"You really are not a morning person, are you?" mum had said resignedly.

She had learnt not to bite or take offence at my ways, most of the time, and would tactically ignore me- giving me space. She suspected that I had an issue with something and knew that it would spill out like an unmanned water hydrant at some point- possibly unleashing damage on those around me or possibly quenching a much-needed thirst. It had taken me a few months to admit one of the issues which I had about being a secondary school student. It hadn't really involved the school itself either, but none of the things that bothered me were usually rational- or so I have since been told.

I had hated the journey to school- but outright refused to get a bus. I had once tried a bus and Dad had walked the 'school to the bus stop' route with me. He wasn't to have known that the bus route had terminated at the stop he showed me and that I would try and walk home. I had become lost in a housing estate; a rabbit warren of roads had made me lose my bearings. Each road had mirrored the last and I was feeling penned in. It was as if I had been travelling deeper and deeper into a trap from which there was no escape. Like Alice falling down the rabbit hole, I had been bewildered in a land I hadn't recognised. I had phoned him in a state of hysteria. I couldn't even tell him where I was. Immediately after this incident, Dad had installed a tracker on my phone. I have honestly never been on a public bus since..

The car journey to school had always been a form of hell. To begin with, the car itself was ridiculously small for my four siblings and my mum- yet she refused to drive the family MPV. She was not ever the best at driving and said that the 'large' car used to drive her- which I told her was actually impossible- but she stuck with the Corsa nonetheless. So, we all had clambered in. I had always taken the seat in the front- always. Mum used to say it was because I was the oldest and the tallest, but she knew that I could not have coped squashed in the back with the siblings. They had quarrelled and pushed and shoved. The child car seat had often dug into the child sitting next to it - mum had usually yelled at them all before we had even pulled out of our tarmac drive. I had sat in the front and frowned. There would be little conversation from me. I had PE and food tech on the same day which meant I might have far too many things to carry. My bags had wrapped around my legs and it felt like they had been set in concrete; an effective murder method if I had been thrown in the sea. I had momentarily imagined myself sinking through the foamy swash and passing the floating brown-green seaweed as I made my way to the seabed. I quickly paused the channel in my mind- I hadn't been in the mood for such thoughts. I had tried to move my legs again, but the entrapment had still been in place. If mum had crashed the car- which was possible with her track record- I would have been finished. Paralysed. My legs would have been crushed amongst the cake tins and PE trainers. Would people visit me in hospital? I had imagined that I'd be bought gifts- maybe a new lip balm? Chocolates? I imagined the sound of crunching metal before forcing myself to switch the channels in my mind for a second time in quick succession that morning.

Sullenly, I had sat in the front whilst we had completed the drop off- the ten-year-old first, then the six-year-old and finally onwards to the secondary school. All through year 7, mum had stopped the car and had actually walked me across the main road- I was not road savvy in the slightest. One time, a car on my left waved me to cross and I hadn't thought to look in the other direction. A hoot resounded.... Mum had later said that her heart was in her mouth; I had to correct her though. The heart was on the left-hand side- possibly slightly more in the middle of the upper chest to be precise.

Soon traffic lights had appeared outside of the school- I guess the school must have campaigned for more road safety crossing measures but they hadn't helped to settle my nerves. In a way, they had made me become more agitated because it meant that I was expected to navigate myself across the road. Mum had then parked just past the lights, and hurriedly said her goodbyes- she was in a rush to get to work. I hated the traffic lights, because usually someone had just pressed the button and beaten me. By the time I had exited the car, they were on red again- glowing menacingly. Instead of just being able to cross, I had to stand and anticipate the crossing. So, I stood and waited nervously, becoming more anxious by the second. It had felt like an eternity waiting for the green man to appear and I hesitated in fear that the cars wouldn't actually stop. What if they hadn't noticed the green man? What if I hadn't been able to cross the road in time? What if I had misread the signs? It had not been as if I was crossing a rope bridge above a deep chasm, crocodiles snapping their hungry jagged jaws menacingly below, but it was the first hurdle to overcome before I even got into school. Red, red & amber, green, amber and then red. Red for danger. Red for embarrassment. School had told me that red was symbolic for sex too- but there had been nothing sexy about crossing that road.

Routinely, I had been the school student who arrived early. I had frequented the same place every day and my teachers had known where to find me. I had enjoyed the quiet at this time- it had been like school in slow motion. I had always arrived a good 40 minutes before school officially began but nobody had ever moved me on; I guess I was like part of the furniture- I had camouflaged well against the backdrop of the metal lockers. Dull, silent and no trouble. There had been a calming feeling about getting into school early. The quiet and serene atmosphere would soon be broken by the incoming tide of students, but I had sat crossed legged on the carpet and been thankful. I had watched the sunrise of the school day begin. The gentle lapping of the tide would soon become a torrent; undulated waves would soon clash and destroy that peace…..but I had felt ready for it.

Sitting in front of the lockers, I had read or played on my phone- maybe scrolled through Instagram. Either activity had suited me, as I would have been left alone with which ever one I had chosen: both allowed me to become introverted, lost in my own company. Happy in my own company. I hadn't commented much, nor added any of my own comments on social media really, but I had looked at everyone else's post with a keen interest. There might have been a new outfit that sparked my interest......

Punctuality was also my thing. I had never been late to class- a thing which annoyed my best friend when we were placed in different classes. I had refused to wait for her as I was more anxious about arriving late to class, than her wrath or feelings of rejection. The bell had given five minutes to get to class and that was what I used that time for- of course. If I left on the second bell, then that meant I would have been late- it meant I hadn't followed the rules of the bells. What was the point of the bells if no one took any notice of them?

"Hey, wait up!" my friend had hollered.

"No." I had replied bluntly.

Resolutely, I had swung my backpack on my shoulders and marched to class. Had she been following? Had I even cared?

In terms of what I looked like, I had done well to fit in at school. I had achieved the 'average' school girl look- I hadn't overly stood out for the right or wrong reasons. Fortunately, I had had an older cousin at the same school to advise me. When I had started year 7- my school skirt was already shorter than most. I had seen the other newbies with kilts down to their ankles and thought how odd they looked. It was as if they had shrunk and were wearing outsized clothes- or clothes that would fit an adult. Nobody bought their casual clothes three sizes to large so why on earth had they bought a school uniform that wouldn't fit them until leaver's day? For me, the less fabric the better- I would have hated swathes of fabric wrapping around my calves. The year 7 students screamed "I'm new!" and I was so pleased that I had been given inside information on what not to look like. I had mingled in with the majority and hadn't looked so 'fresh'. I had clocked the typical skirt length, the type of footwear which people wore and the bags they had. My observation skills had never failed me. I had refused a new kilt ever since I had started and still wore the same one four years later. My kilt had been like an old friend except it kept getting shorter as I my legs grew in length. We had rows about it at home.

"I can literally see your backside" Mum chastised, "at least wear tights- it really is far too short."

 "Tights make my legs itch.. and everyone else wear skirts this short."

"You wear tights for ballet classes, so what is the difference?"

A lot of difference actually: ballet tights were soft and had been purposely created to allow for as much flexibility and movement as possible. They had a soft waistband and a seamless gusset that was invisible under leotards. Typical black school tights had a scratchy tight waistband- it was as if the Lycra became more brittle every time they were washed. They 'balled' in the wash too and after they had been worn once or twice, lacked the same softness and smoothness that they had when they were new. 'Supersoft tights'- hardly.

"Well I will just have to buy you a new longer one- that is indecent!" she had threatened.

Yawn. We had had this row before- so many times. She knew it was futile, but I guess must have felt guilty condoning its length. She felt the need to comment on it, despite knowing that I would not wear a new skirt. I had become accustomed to the school kilt I wore, how it sat on my hips, the worn leather buckle on the second hole, third if I had overindulged on cake. I had told her that I would not go to school if she swapped my kilt- she knew I hadn't been kidding either. I hadn't done that- I couldn't do that. Jokes and teasing were not part of my repertoire, actually. Eventually, we compromised and I wore shorts underneath the skirt. Everyone else had. I had noticed, of course I had.

Food tech had been one of my favourite lessons. I used to think about food a lot and I enjoyed following recipes and reading the instructions. There had been an order and precision in this lesson. Rules that must be obeyed: health and safety had been a necessary expectation. I felt most at home behind the sink and worktop- the only off-putting thing had been the trace of stale odours that had often lingered from the day before. Like a hound trailing a scent, I could detect garlic and an acrid smell which must have meant disaster for some student or other.

I hadn't always had a partner to work alongside with when our classes became GCSE- but I coped with that. Sometimes I had joined a three and sometimes I had worked alone. It had often been easier not having to compromise or pretend to be happy turn taking. On my own, it was always my way. Less frustration-less pretence. My cooking teacher had no idea of my struggles though- if my cooking result hadn't looked quite like the recipe photo it plagued my day. I once made chicken drumsticks from a whole chicken which I had dissected the week before. The teacher had frozen the pieces and then defrosted them, ready for class on the following Monday. Breadcrumbs at the ready, I had enthusiastically set to work. I had studied the recipe and if followed- felt that it should all turn out as stated, right? Step one... sorted. Step two... done. I had begun to fry them gently in the pan only to have a red watery liquid ooze out and then bubble and boil. The teacher had come over to see what I was exclaiming about. I was pretty sure that this hadn't been part of the plan. It had not mentioned this in the recipe instructions. She agreed that it wasn't supposed to do this and then sadly watched me as I followed her next instructions. I scraped the breadcrumbs and chicken from the pan into the waste bin. My heart had tumbled in there after them. I looked at the raw red blood settling with the oil and my heart wept inside.

I have never since coped when recipes hadn't worked out. I had been intending to have these for lunch and upset settled as it dawned on me that I would just have to stick with my grilled chicken salad. I knew my intended creation was not quite KFC, but possibly the next best thing. Sullenly, I had tidied up my station area- and begrudgingly, I joined in the food appraisal at the end. Everyone else's had worked and did indeed look like the delicious takeaway that I had been planning on having. I had stood back behind the rest of the group and tried hard to mask the tears which I had felt pricking in my eyes. Who actually cried at chicken at my age? This disappointment had set my mood off all day. I had still been morose when I arrived home at 5pm, it had become worse as each hour surpassed. I had been unable to conceal my disappointment any longer. I sobbed, I cried and was marginally hysterical as I relayed the story to mum.

"Sounds like the chicken was still frozen and as you heated it- you thawed it," she explained. "Not your fault love, if your chicken had been fresh, it seems like it would have been fine."

She had definitely been no cook, but this was the explanation I had needed about 7 hours ago. It had made sense as to why there was a sudden pool of watery blood; why the chicken had looked like a mauled victim floating in the middle of the bloodbath. Disappointment could overwhelm me. I hadn't coped well, and it totally consumed me when what I was expecting to happen, hadn't. I would contain my emotions in front of friends and at school, just, but keeping the pot simmering for hours just spoiled the taste. It was not good practice and not heathy for my mind. It only later erupted like a pressure cooker at some point. Some poor bystander, oblivious to earlier events, would get caught in the furore and wonder what the hell was wrong with me, and what the hell they had done?

At times, I had felt like the stupid one in class- but I knew I wasn't stupid. I was at grammar school and had decent scores. That was enough clarification for me to accept that I had a reasonable level of intelligence. Despite this though, I always used to feel that I had to work that little bit harder than others, that I had to really concentrate and focus. All my school reports had praised these qualities, but I had regarded them as failures. I wanted to chat in class and not listen- just like my clever friends did. I hadn't been able to though, as I always followed what the teacher requested. I always had to listen that little bit harder too. Understanding their commands caused me difficulty more often than I would like to admit.

"Is that the answer?" I might have whispered.

"Yes."

"Is it actually?"

Perhaps I had struggled with all the different teachers at secondary- they all had their different ways and expectations. I had struggled to connect with most of them but had my favourites. My form tutor in year 11 had been my saviour and had managed to assist me through what felt like the most stressful year at school that I have had to date. Mum had already been into school about me and my 'quirks', so I had wondered if others knew or even cared? Although I had been placed on the school SEN register, my teachers had never said anything about it, and I never noticed them trying to make my life that little bit easier. Maybe I wouldn't have noticed- subtlety had never been my thing either.

At first, I had liked to sit at the front of the class- I lip read and found this useful in helping me understand. I had done this for years. People thought I avoided looking at their eyes, but it had in fact been because I was focused on their mouths. I had no idea why I did it, but it helped me understand somehow. Maybe it was like when I danced: I watched how the moves corresponded to the sounds. Perhaps unwittingly, I had become accustomed to doing the same in school. I had watched the mouth formations which corresponded to the sounds made and the words used- and took my meaning from that. So no- I hadn't 'eye balled' the teacher or held their gaze, but I had noticed their cracked lips and coldsore; the fine black hairs above their upper lip which needed threading. I should have advised a lip balm-I was knowledgeable in that area- but it would have appeared rude.

Some teachers really hadn't helped, but I guess I was just one in a class of many faces. It would seem fortunate if they knew all our names- getting them to know the entire class' idiosyncrasies was maybe an expectation too far. They had caused me such confusion. Some asked me questions which I hadn't thought were questions: I had no idea about the answer they were searching for. I had been honestly dumbfounded at times.

"Is Joe in your class?" one had queried.

"Erm," I faltered. I giggled and had looked at my friend for help- but she gave none.

"Well..?" he queried again.

"Erm-" I had again repeated.

"Ask a simple question!" he had muttered as he moved onto the next table, clearly irritated by my insufficient response.

To me though, this was not a simple question. Which Joe had he been meaning? I knew two: Joseph (Joe) and Joanna (Jo). Both were in different classes. Which class had he meant when he had asked that question? If he had meant my English class, then the answer would have been no to Joe but yes to Jo. If he had said 'science class'- it might have been yes if he was actually referring to Joanna. But if he meant Joseph then it was a no again……and which class did he actually mean? I had nearly nine different classes and lessons.

I had experienced a similar situation at the Doctors. Mum had taken me to have a chat about ASD. She and Dad had talked to me about my 'funny little ways' which had actually helped. Sometimes, having the obvious pointed out, could be quite eye opening….. or equally devastating. By the age of 12, secondary school had put some support in: social skills workshops and they had advised that a discussion with the family Doctor might be helpful. It hadn't been though. Far from it.

I had just done sports day on the day of my scheduled appointment and was wearing my orange house top. The Doctor had asked me questions about my hobbies- my dancing.

"So, you have friends?" he queried.

"Yes" I had replied.

"Social media?"

"Yes," I had replied.

I did have social media-of course I had- I had noticed that everyone my age had. He had congratulated me for being sociable, yet he hadn't asked me if I actually socialised on it though. I hadn't- not until several years later. I used it as a doorway into the world of others. I simply sat and would read through everyone else's posts and look and take note. I had been like the wallflower at a party: invited, but still an outsider -looking in. Incidentally, the Doctor's son had attended my school and was actually in my year, or so he explained. I remembered being confused by this small chit chat. I hadn't cared who his son was- I hadn't known his son. I had become irritated and anxious- what had been the point of this conversation? I smiled and had pretended to look interested, of course. He had later asked what my house was and then I stumbled. I had looked over at my mum. Confusion had clouded my mind. I lived in a bungalow at that point- what on earth had he meant when he asked what my house was? I hadn't lived in a house for a couple of years by then. After what had felt like a lifetime of awkward silence, mum had saved me.

She intervened, "You're in Curie aren't you? Your *school* house?"

Ah- I had got it. I had all the right answers, but unfortunately, I have learnt that people hadn't always asked the right questions.

I had stopped sitting at the front of the class, as I moved ranks through the year groups. I began to prefer to sit at the back or the side where I could see what was happening around me. Heads had bobbed up and down and I wondered if they had taken such notice of my hair when they had sat behind me. I watched the hairstyles and grimaced at those who I thought needed to wash their hair- I was fastidious with my own. I had noticed the grease and wetness- I imagined the smell of roast lamb and had felt my stomach knot.

There had been more space too if I sat further away from the front teacher's desk. In one class I had a naughtier boy sit next to me. He had been a constant distraction and I was irritated when he chewed or tapped his pen. I knew that he had been sat next to me deliberately because I was a model student. Of course I was.

"Here, sit next to this young lady," the teacher had reprimanded, "she might teach you some manners about how to conduct yourself in class."

I had hated being sat next to people I hadn't liked or known. Why should I have had to put up with them? Why had teachers thought that this was okay? Invariably, these particular students would want to borrow my pens, as they hadn't been organised enough to sort themselves out, clearly. It was not my fault if they hadn't brought a pen- but I usually relented. My stationery set was unrivalled: I had everything I would possibly need and more. Another collection. However, resentment and panic had started to accumulate, as my mouth had replied 'yes' to a request to use my possessions. This had been despite my mind screaming 'No', yelling at them to get their dirty hands and filthy fingernails off my things. I have already said that I was a performer, and I absolutely deserved an Oscar for the self-restraint I had displayed as I watched my pens getting chewed: enamel teeth clamping into the soft plastic lids leaving marks. It would have been rude to make a fuss- no one else was so protective of their belongings- so I let them keep them. There had been no way that I would have allowed a damaged and contaminated pen back in my pencil case, to roll around with the others and spread the germs. I had shuddered as my glue stick had been over wound up and I had discreetly blocked my ears when it was rubbed vigorously across the page- it had made a weird sticky noise like suction that made my stomach churn.

Besides the pen grievance, some of the students who had been placed next to me smelled pretty poor too. Tinge of dog or 'parfum de unwashed' clothes. It had made me feel sick and distracted my focus. Mum had offered to write a school note explaining my displeasure, but I had asked her not to. I had been wearing the mask at school and maybe that would filter out the scents: my own invisible PPE. Anyway, I had an abundance of body sprays I could have utilised if the situation had become too unmanageable for me. I had the full range- from 'Secret Desires' to 'Vanilla Mist'....of course I had. I had doused myself in them; my pungent aroma of 'Pure Seduction' had been more powerful than their scent of 'Dirty Hamster' or 'Wet Mouldy Wash'. All the time I was surrounded by my clouds of sweet-smelling mists, I could not smell their dank sagging rain clouds. I hadn't much cared that some of my peers claimed to be asthmatic, as I sprayed liberally in the classroom. They hadn't needed to breath it in and anyway, they would have had an inhaler. It wouldn't have been my fault if they had forgotten to take it to school with them. They should have been more prepared.

Chpt 8: The role of 'The sister'

My relationship with my siblings had been what I would regard as reasonably good. I'm not going to lie, I had hated them some days- or I might have hated one of them for a week. It might have alternated. The following week a different sibling would have been on my target list.

"Enough." Mum said assertively.

It had made no difference; I had been on a ride and was not about to get off any time soon. Like a lumberjack, I kept chipping away at the tree, hitting it a bit further and a little harder each time. I would wipe the sweat from my brow and pause to take stock of the situation, but I hadn't rested until that tree was cut, hurt if you will, and was lying on the ground defeated. There had been many times when we had got on so well. I had felt loved and popular- they had wanted to sleep in my room on holiday nights and the four of us would camp. I would still have my double bed and possibly allow the youngest to share it if she had promised to not move or wriggle- but the other two had no choice but to sleep on the floor. I still had my rain noises playing on my Echo Dot and my tiny bathroom window remained open; I was insensitive to whether they were chilly or not. My room: my rules. I had the biggest room out of us all and the en-suite. Did my siblings mind? I hadn't given it a thought- I was the eldest. Simple.

Some days I had rowed continuously with them: They had been watching what I hadn't wanted to watch, or one of them had eaten the last of the cereal, or one of them had taken my hairbands..... or one was simply breathing. There hadn't needed to be a rhyme or reason. If I were to be honest, my anger and annoyance at them would no doubt have been over something completely unrelated. But I hadn't known that at the time. They would have been innocent on most occasions, oblivious bystanders, but it has been said that 'we hurt the ones we love'. Except that I had never touched them or beaten them, so maybe that is not the right phrase.

When I had been younger the arguments had seemed quite frequent. I had argued more with my brother who was just two years younger- the girls were younger still and I knew to be nice to little ones. I had seen everyone fuss them and treat them kindly so naturally I had copied. I left them alone mostly. The situation with my brother had been a little different. My brother had left his Lego build on the floor in the lounge which I had kicked- accidentally- when I walked in. He was upset because I had just ruined it and wasted the last two hours of his time. There had been a shattering noise and plastic had crumbled; pieces of vibrant Lego had skidded across the flooring. He had become very upset but nobody had seemed to notice my upset. I had hurt my foot which was far more serious than a broken Lego build. The agony from standing on a Lego piece has to be the same as giving birth- I had heard that that was supposed to be very painful too- not that anyone had given ME any sympathy.

"You've just ruined it" my brother had said irritably. "Look where you're going."

"No I haven't and actually, I WAS looking where I was going" I replied.

"I've got to rebuild that part now!"

"And? Don't leave it on the rug then."

I had rarely used to say sorry. Most of the time though, it hadn't been my fault so why would I have apologised? Other times, I had argued with my parents and then they would start arguing with themselves. I had been like a boil that needed to be lanced. Burst it and clean it, otherwise I would just turn the skin around it an angry reddish purple. What might start as a small spot, would build up if allowed and soon there would be an infected wound.

"Go and blow your nose" I demanded at my brother as he ate his breakfast.

"No- I'm eating."

"Well no one wants to listen to you snorting and snuffling," I had snarled.

"Go somewhere else then."

"It's disgusting. Snort snort. Can't you breathe properly? You sound like a pig in a trough."

"Go somewhere else then."

"It's gross. Do you eat like that at school? Would you eat like that at your friends? No wonder you don't have a girlfriend. Would you eat like that in front of one? It's disgusting. You've got half a cereal box in that bowl- I can hear you heavy breathing as if your nose is all blocked...."

I was off. Insults, questions.... I have always needed stopping at the start. Treat the wood- stop the rot before it began. Once it had taken a hold, who was to measure the extent of damage that might be caused? The irritation would set in and I would keep on about it like a dog with a bone. I needed to be put on a leash, muzzled possibly. I had needed help from someone to stop me.

However, if I had been in public, I wouldn't have dared to comment. How rude would that have been? I had watched my friend as she ate her 8 Weetabix and not utter a single word, as my body slowly changed colour to match the sleek white and grey shades of her kitchen.

Had I been jealous of them at times? Yes. Although, retrospectively, I was probably the one who received special treatment. If they had done something well at school or at their dancing, I was unable to be complimentary.

"So?" I had shrugged. I used to genuinely find being pleased for other people hard- or if I knew that I should display that kind of reaction- my efforts would seem hyperbolic, forced.... fake even. I had risked sounding sarcastic. Mum used to try and reason with me and encourage me.

"Oh isn't that lovely!" she had said say to me to encourage a positive reaction. I would look at the infant school certificate 'Awarded for best handwriting', my younger sister waiting proudly and expectantly.

"No. You're still not joining your letter f up correctly" I had replied. I hadn't been criticising- I was stating the obvious and her tall letter stems weren't tall enough either.

"Well I think you've done very well," Mum had encouraged and taken my sister to put her card certificate on to the fridge door.

I had just been awarded a level 7 in my English essay and that hadn't been pinned on the fridge with a magnet, had it? Mum had congratulated me for that but hadn't offered to display it. I had scowled and gone to my room to read. It was my magnet too- I had bought it on the school trip to Germany last year. I had toyed with the idea of reclaiming it. Sharing's not caring. What's mine is mine.

Chpt 9: The role of 'The food critic'

Cake, carrot cake to be precise, had been my downfall at times. By the time I had hit mid-teens, I had formed a little habit. Every day I had queued at the school canteen for a piece of carrot cake. I had waited anxiously in line, wondering if there would still be a slice left for me. I eyed up the person in front- judging them. Had they looked like a carrot cake person? I had stretched my neck and tried to calculate the number of people in the queue- if they all wanted a piece- would there be enough? I had felt resentment growing. Stress. Anxiety. Someone had pushed in. "Er you can't push in" I had said righteously.

I hadn't got slapped but I might easily have done. I had finally reached the counter and to my relief there had still been carrot cake left. I knew if there hadn't been, a dark cloud would have followed me overhead for the remainder of the day. People might have noticed. They might have wondered, but they would never have connected my feelings with the disappointment of not being able to buy a piece of cake. I had been in luck though, and had taken my cake and followed my friends to where we usually sat. Same place, same seating area.

I never devoured my food. I sat the slice of cake firmly on the table and had positioned myself comfortably. This had become a little ritual, a part of the day that I had looked forward to. I had noted the swathes of the cream cheese icing and the soft spongy look of the cake- glistening slightly from the oil and grease from which it had been baked. I had been lucky- this slice had a complete orange shaped fondant carrot placed on top. It had annoyed me when the canteen cut through it- they never managed to do it symmetrically. I had picked my slice up and delicately took a mouthful; a warm sensation flooded my body. Delicious. As always.

At times, I had watched the boys in the group eat like my brother, but of course, I never commented to them. I had never criticised, despite their table manners being despicable. They had disgusted me actually. They had eaten voraciously- like hyenas from the documentaries, or as if somehow, they were ravenous and had just escaped solitary confinement. They had used their hands to wipe fragments and morsels from their mouths and then take a huge glug of drink from their cans or bottles- as if dampening a fire in the pit of their stomachs. I had tried to focus on my own food but once I had noticed something, it was hard to reverse the image.

I had been so different- I ate delicately and enjoyed every morsel- to me, food was an experience. Taste it, savour it, enjoy it.

I also had taken notice of what my friends had. I had been interested. Some were uber healthy, some hideously unhealthy and then those who maintained they were healthy who in fact were not. I had told my mum about it later and my annoyance was palpable- food was absolutely becoming something that caused me pleasure or displeasure.

"She had two bits of pizza and then ate a yoghurt- saying she was on a diet?" I had said incredulously. "Then got cookies out!"

Why had food always irritated me? Why had I become the judge and jury of the school lunches? Had it been because I had started to put on weight- all that cake- and I was unhappy about my developing shape? Had I been jealous and resentful that I was trying to be more healthy- that my own mum hadn't allowed me to have pizza for lunch daily? I knew I had to stop my cake habit, but like an addict, there was nothing better than a hit. My clothes had been getting tighter and the school skirt I had worn for years was starting to not fit. I had moved it up a notch again. It had worried me that I would have to get a new one. I tried desperately to be healthy with food choices, but I had been insatiable at times. I had needed to experience the feeling of being full. What I ate needed to 'feel' worth the calories consumed-the fix needed to be strong enough. If I ate something and it hadn't triggered that feeling of satisfaction, then I had moved onto the next option. What else was around that would taste good? My tastes changed too frequently though. I had decided that I really liked tuna and jacket potato and the next time I was served tuna, I would refuse to eat it because it smelt too fishy. Gravy left a dry taste on the roof of my mouth. Mum's cooking had been pretty basic but then I guess I had been a pretty harsh critic.

Back at school, I had sat in our lunch time circle and feel resentment. Resentment at their pizza, or greasy ham and cheese melt, resentment at my grilled chicken salad- fresh out of a shop bought cellophane container. (Even though I had specifically requested it.) I hadn't used Tupperware for a few years- by that time I was age 15. I had hated the fact that when the lid of a Tupperware box was peeled open, there was a musty smell, whether it had been through the dishwasher or not. I had imagined that it might be like the scent of a coffin being opened: a sweet cloying mouldy smell. A dirty smell. I had imagined that the contents that had been fresh when placed in there, then decomposed and began to rot once the lid had been sealed. I had gone through a stage of only eating lunch which was factory prepared. Each punnet of fruit would have to be an individual portion or container- with a clear cellophane wrapper that could be pulled off neatly when it was lunchtime. It had screamed hygiene, cleanliness, food health and safety regulations. Best before date. Use by. Hair nets and plastic gloves had prepared it.

I had never asked for anyone else's food. I would look at their pizza enviously, but would never have asked my friends if I could have had a bite. Never. So why had my friends decided it was acceptable to just take my fruit? I knew a punnet looked quite large but by the time six people had delved into it- there was never an awful lot left. Grapes had been tinged with orange dust from one of their Dorito fingers. I imagined the grease from the pepperoni and remembered distinctly what my uncle had said:

'Maltesers are supposed to be shiny. '

If they had been dull and matt in appearance, then they would have been touched too many times within the share bag. I had looked at my spoiled fruit with disdain bubbling just beneath the surface. How many of these grapes were now dull and matt?

"Finish them if you like" I had said; I had taken my shiny lip gloss out of my makeup bag and reapplied the smile, painting over the angry mouth that had been at risk of frothing and ranting.

I had been irritable for the remainder of the day-a little hungry and disgruntled- but I think my friends were getting used to my moods. If they weren't, it hadn't bothered me anyway.

Chpt 10: The end of the Show

I must admit that I think I am at my happiest at this point in my life. I know who I am. I am Lottie, age 17 and 11 months. It is as if it has taken me years to practise and try different roles before finding one that has suited me. I have dabbled in many, worn many different costumes and painted my face many a time. I like to think that I have many sides to me but the main one- the one I present now- is the real one. The real me- without labels, without facades and without fear. The only performance you will see now is the one on the actual stage. And when you see me up there, please realise that the huge smile is genuine- glossy and red, of course- but real. It's not a trick of makeup either- my blue shining eyes are glistening with joy and not tears.

I think accepting that I have quirks and 'funny ways' was the turning point for me, actually. The 'serious' chat with my parents when I was nearly age 13 helped me see that my behaviour was at times irrational and at times valid- but talking enabled me to discuss my reasoning too. I had the security and support to explain what I felt and how the thought of a burglar was so real to me. Or fire, even. In turn they would help me reason through my worries. I am able to be honest sooner instead of bottling up pent up frustrations. I can accept disappointment more reasonably. I recognise now when I am becoming obsessive about things- it doesn't stop me- but I feel more in control, somehow. I spoke openly and honestly for the first time in years: with the family and with friends. We now laugh about things, we avoid things, we prepare me for things- we try things.

I'm not going to lie, but even at my age now, I still have my 'funny little ways' although I don't refer to them as that anymore. There's nothing funny or odd about them. It's just my way- what I do and who I am. Even on our recent family trip to Disney, I experienced anxiety about certain rides: The Haunted House, Tower of Terror- both involved enclosed spaces and evoked images of entrapment and claustrophobia. I agreed to go on them though- I can rationalise so much better now. I can accept known knowns- things that I know I know, whereas before I would imagine an infinite number of unknowns. So many possible scenarios and eventualities would race through my mind- things that might or might not occur. I have learnt not to worry about the unknown happenings of life. They can't be planned for so why worry? Why try and visualise something that might never happen? I'm not there yet, but small steps and all…...

"There are no windows or doors: get out if you can…" the words threatened from the Haunted House ride.

There would have been a time when I would have taken that statement literally. I would have cried and clung onto my dad- my younger siblings not even reacting- realising that this was all part of the ride and part of the act.

But I know now- I am learning to think with a more rational mind. I know that a commercial ride wouldn't allow the customers to be trapped- there would need to be fire exits and safety exit points. There would be a fire alarm system and sprinklers- health and safety regulations. Stop, drop and roll- I know what to do in an emergency now anyway.

I have accepted that these thoughts and feelings are what makes me the person I am- those who know me don't mind. If they do mind, I still don't really care. It's more certain than not, that if I have bothered someone, then they aren't in my life at this moment. They will have chosen to walk away as others have done in my past. Their loss- I will no longer change for anybody.

I still trip up. Life still throws me a curveball as they say, but I can deal with that. I can laugh- the smile is natural and not painted. My colour doesn't change.

I still get lost in conversations at times. I still struggle to pick up on nuances and subtle meanings- but the analysis skills I am learning for A level English are ones I can try to use in real life too. Instead of just lip reading now I have my tool kit: I look at gesture, body language, trying to recognise tone, choice of words and always, if uncertain, I have my fall-back method- Is it actually? It doesn't always save me but might just give me time to tread water before I drown.

I try and banter with adults and invariably get it wrong but have accepted that this is part of growing up.

"Let me run you home, have a drink" Mum tried to persuade my Aunty. "Seriously, let me run you home."

"As if you can run!" I had laughed loudly. "You can't even run to the end of the road."

At least I am confident enough to have these conversations now-rather than hiding in a book, I just read for pleasure.

School is settling and I move into year 13 with a strong friendship group – I join in on social media more frequently and we chat for a prolonged time on messenger- even if I just listen I still feel included. Don't get me wrong- they can irritate me at times, but I guess I annoy the hell out of them too. I can choose to accept or decline calls knowing that they won't think any less of me for doing so- and anyway, we will just speak for longer next time. There is a natural honesty- an acceptance that we all tolerate one another. I have genuine feelings for them- any pretence has dissipated, and I feel complete when with them. There is no need to hide- and if I did try to, I know they would find me.

Sixth form continues to challenge me, still:

Science question-

Nabil wants to work out the density of a pebble. He has a displacement can and a beaker. What other piece of equipment will he need?

Apparently, my answer of a 'pebble' was incorrect but, as far as I am concerned, it didn't actually state that Nabil already had a pebble- he just 'wanted to work out the density' of one. I want to eat a chocolate bar, but it doesn't mean I actually have one, does it? Mum just laughed and said maybe a pebble didn't fall in the category of 'equipment'. But I disagree- he clearly needs a pebble if he wants to work out the density of one. And more importantly, who is Nabil? Should he always get what he wants?

I'm still pretty much the same person but possibly more wholesome- I have matured with age- but not like a cheese or wine, mind. It turns out that I didn't need a label to know how to handle me- just care, kindness and a little extra understanding has been sufficient. There is a naïve honesty and openness that I have now, where all sides are visible to see and experience.

I rarely wear much make up these days- I don't feel the need. My bare fresh face smiles back at me in the mirror- no more painted clown and invisible tears. And anyway, I have discovered a new range of face creams, cleansers, day cream, overnight creams, masks and scrubs…..I can feel another collection coming on.

Printed in Great Britain
by Amazon

38736675R00047